OPTRICKS 2

BY MELINDA WENTZELL
AND D.K. HOLLAND

TROUBADOR PRESS
SANFRANCISCO

The optical illusion on the front cover is created by a sequential grid progression and vertical displacement. The displacement (or shifting) of the grid serves to enclose the number 2. The color combination and the equal areas of both orange and pink cause a "shimmer" effect.

The illusion on the back cover is a double version of Necker's cube. Mr. Necker first developed his cube about 1832. The cubes have a "reversible" quality due to the one point perspective in which they are drawn. Stare at the cubes for a while and you will see them suddenly reverse direction right before your eyes; i.e. from one point of view the smaller cube seems contained by the larger and from the other point of view the smaller cube seems to be outside of the larger one.

Book designed
by Gorilla Graphics
San Francisco

Whatever meets the eye, meets the brain as well. It's this interaction that determines what we see and how we see it. When the eye and brain alter what we see, an optical illusion occurs. OPTRICKS 2 deals with optical illusions—of which there are two basic types:

1

Abstract Illusions usually consist of basic geometric shapes with which no intellectual associations are made—like the example of grouping on page 13 or Zollner's Illusion on page 31.

2

Reality Illusions (and the degree to which they work) are dependent on previous associations—such as the painting by Magritte on page 11 or the computer gargoyle on page 21.

Some illusions appear to be a combination of the two basic types described. The effect of the bird in the bird cage on page 6 is actually an abstract illusion, since the same effect could be achieved by using basic geometric shapes. The Necker's cube on the back cover of this book is a reality illusion, since it relies on our knowledge of perspective in order to be effective. It is, however, a basic geometric shape. When you observe each illusion throughout the book, try to judge which is reality and which is abstract.

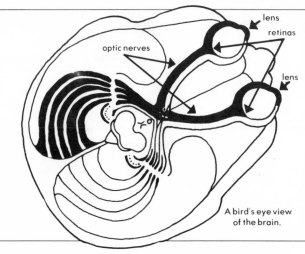

lens
retinas
optic nerves
lens

A bird's eye view of the brain.

The Eye and the Brain. The eye, like a camera, is a hollow vessel containing a light sensitive film (the retina), upon which an image is projected by a lens. In the case of the camera, the projected image is the product, or end result. The eye merely receives the information, which the optic nerve then 'codes' and sends to the brain. As the information passes on into the brain, the codes become more abstract and more complex. Beyond this simple explanation, little is really known about how the brain processes the information it receives.

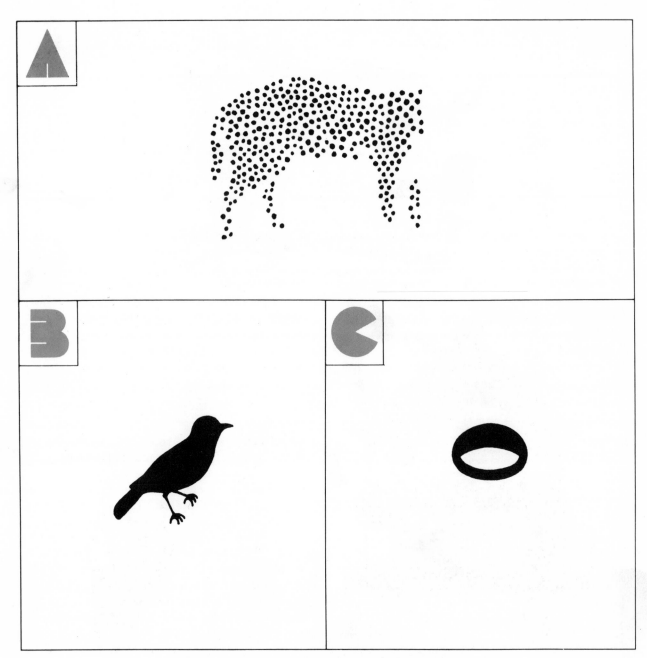

Stare at each image on this page for about one minute . . .

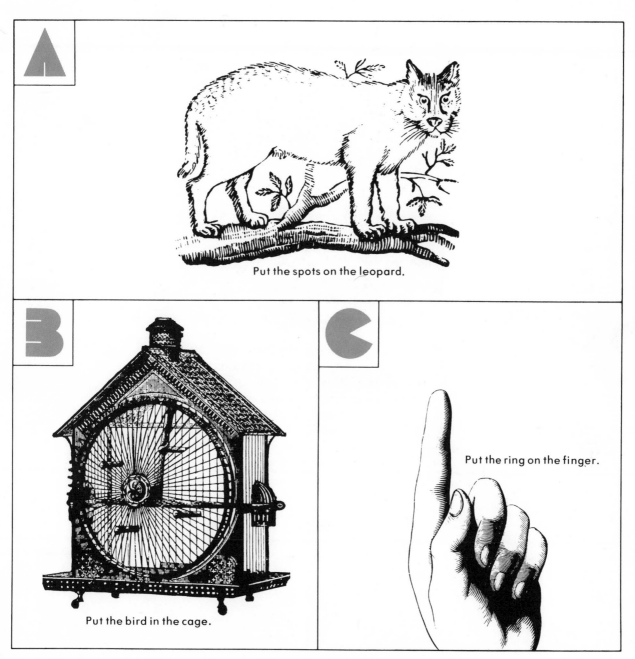

A Put the spots on the leopard.

B Put the bird in the cage.

C Put the ring on the finger.

then stare at its counterpart to complete the picture.

The three seemingly different illusions on the preceding page are actually based on the same optical principle, after-image. When you stare at the images on page 4, the intensity of the black forms against the white page causes your retina to become partially fatigued. The result is a greyish after-image which, when applied to page 5, completes the picture.

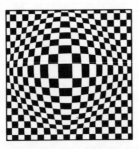 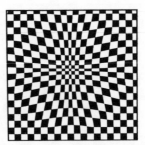

The illusion on page 7, an oil painting by Victor Vasarely, titled "Metagalaxie," is an example of surface distortion. By systematically warping the squares, he creates convex and concave shapes on a two dimensional surface. The equal distribution of black and white cause a shimmer effect. Victor Vasarely is one of the artists responsible for the "Op Art" movement of the 1960's.

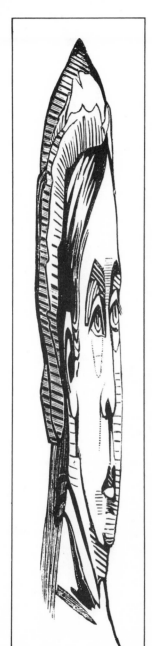   

Why the long faces? Guess who is seen in each portrait.

The four portraits on the preceding page were published in England in 1879. They are, left to right: Queen Victoria, Ben Franklin, and the Princess and Prince of Wales. This illusion is very simple—it is an example of elongated perspective. The words STOP, SLOW and BUS STOP are often painted on roads in this manner. You view them from an angle of about 15 degrees (the average angle of a driver's eyes from the road) instead of 90 degrees (the angle at which you see this paper).

The painting on the preceding page, "Blank Signature," was done by the famous Belgian surrealist Rene Magritte. In it there is a playful exchange between the horse and the trees. Your brain is trained to complete visual images based on past experience; therefore, you strain to imagine a completed horse image which is interrupted by the tree images. Magritte uses a visual paradox to make us believe (if just for a moment) that the scene is logical.

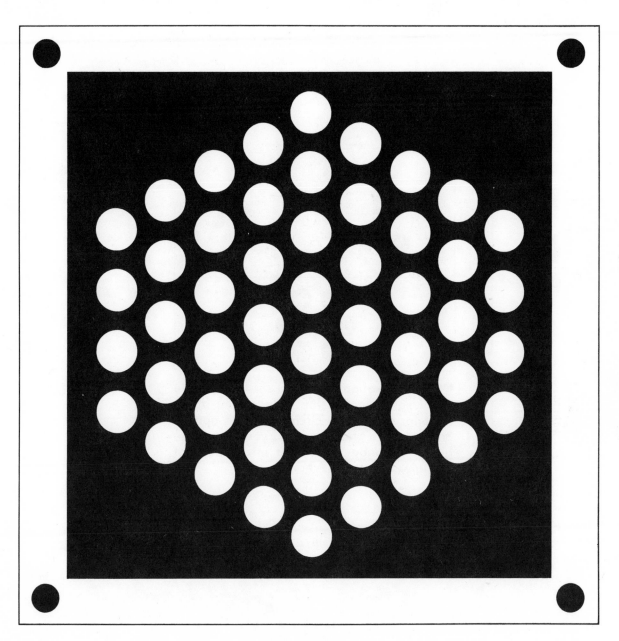

Stare at the circles on this page and see what happens.

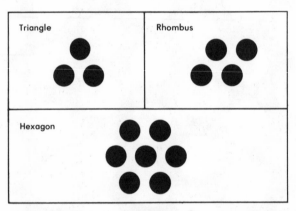

Triangle	Rhombus
Hexagon	

The illustration on page 13 is an example of a grouping illusion. After staring at the page for awhile the circles begin to appear hexagonal in character and your brain begins to arrange the circles into groups of triangles, hexagons, rhombuses.

The lithograph on the preceding page is by the Belgian artist, M. C. Escher and is entitled "Concave and Convex." It is loosely based on the irrational figure known as The Impossible Triangle, pictured above. There are three houses in the scene, each under a vaulted roof. You see the exterior view of the left-hand house, an interior view of the right-hand one and an either exterior or interior view of the one in the middle, depending on how you wish to view it. This is a trick that can only be done two-dimensionally. It plays with your preconceived notions of perspective.

X

By putting your nose on the X you can make the butterfly light on the flower.

The butterfly starts to move toward the flower on page 17 after your nose gets to within about four and a half inches from the X, the point at which your eyes can no longer focus together. You are no longer seeing one image with two separate eyes but two separate images with two separate eyes. Since the actual image you see is controlled by your brain—not by your retina—your brain automatically combines the images to create one simple image.

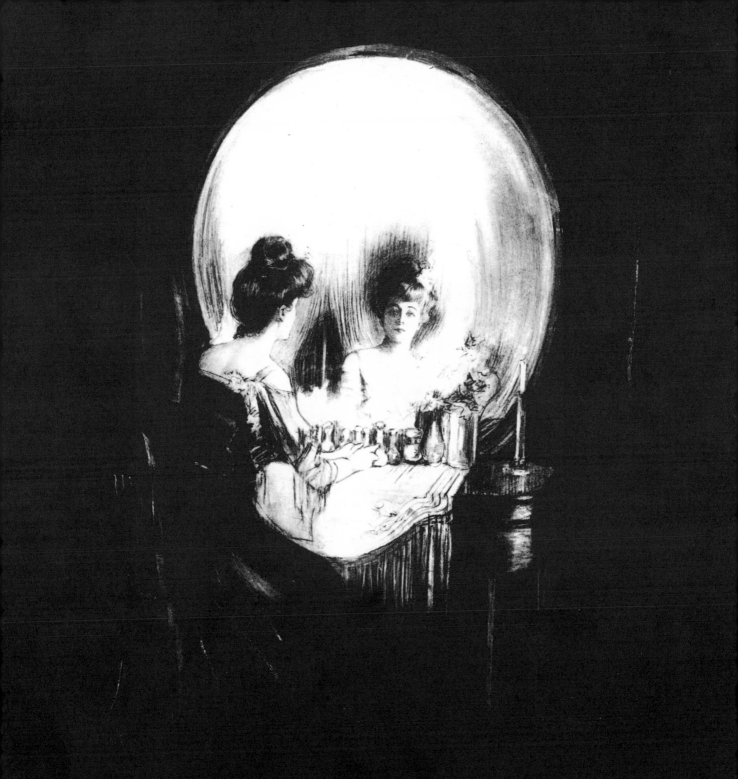

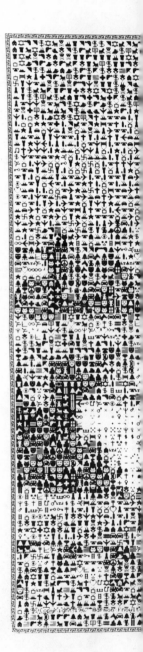

The optical illusion on page 19 was drawn in the 1890's. There are two different perceptual interpretations possible within the illusion. Are there bottles on her dresser, or are the bottles actually the teeth of a skull? Your eyes/brain see it one way, then the other, but it is difficult to see the woman in front of her dresser and the skull at the same time.

21

The computer picture on page 21 was "drawn" from a photograph of the well known gargoyle that sits atop Notre Dame Cathedral overlooking Paris. The computer translated the black, grey, and white areas of the photograph into different dot densities. Then, instead of using dots to represent the areas (as newspapers and magazines do), the computer selected symbols which represent different densities. A house, for instance, may represent a light grey, a face may be equal to a medium grey, and a cat may be the same as a dark grey. Hold the picture at a distance and the symbols will start to blend into the gargoyle's portrait.

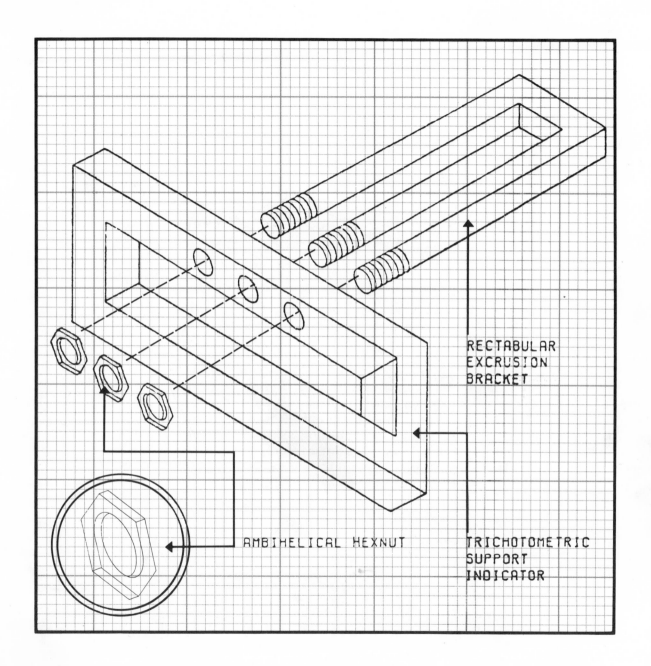

RECTABULAR
EXCRUSION
BRACKET

AMBIHELICAL HEXNUT

TRICHOTOMETRIC
SUPPORT
INDICATOR

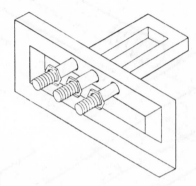

On page 23 you see three irrational figures illustrated as if they could fit together. Each contains two sets of contradictory spatial clues which cause your brain to make two conflicting spatial interpretations. These illusions can only exist in two dimensions since they rely on the absence of depth perception.

Do you see three faces?

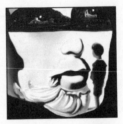

On page 25 you find a painting by Salvadore Dali called "Old Age, Adolescence, Infancy (The Three Ages)." Dali creates the three faces that represent the three ages by using other figures and images; a woman with bowed head, a distant town. Your eyes alternate between the image of the face, and its components. When viewed at close range, the figures of people predominate, when viewed at a distance, the three faces become readily apparent.

"Circle Limit IV (Heaven and Hell)" is the name of the woodcut by M. C. Escher which appears on page 27. It is a clever example of figure-ground reversal. Your eyes alternate between the devils and the angels, neither seems able to dominate. This is because there are equal areas of white and black. Escher creates a second illusion by systematically reducing the size of the images, starting large at the middle, they become mere dots at the outer edge. This makes the circle appear convex. If he had reversed the procedure, the circle would seem to be concave.

The engraving on page 29 was done in 1754 by William Hogarth. Hogarth deliberately misused perspective in different areas of this rural scene. At first glance this looks like a rational, normal picture, but a closer look shows that the actual scene could not be as we see it. There are several visual paradoxes—the fisherman's rod and line, the bridge and the hill and barn. Escher later employed this distortion of perspective in "Concave and Convex" (see page 15).

The effect on page 31 is known as Zollner's illusion. Zollner discovered that short cross strokes cause parallel lines to appear to bend. Any given pair of parallel lines will seem to diverge in the direction that the diagonal lines converge. If you hold the book at an angle, the warping will become even more apparent. A second illusion is present here, called figure-ground. The white areas and black areas are the same and it is impossible to decide which is the figure and which is the background. Zollner discovered his parallel lines illusion while admiring a dress fabric in a women's clothing shop.

Find the Missing Piece of Pie. One piece of pie is missing in the illustration above. To find it, turn the page upside down.

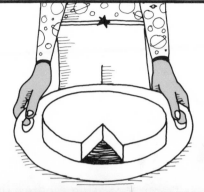

Floating Frankfurter. Place the tips of your index fingers together, holding them about five to eight inches from your nose as the illustration indicates. Look **past** your fingers and focus your eyes on something in the distance. Now separate your fingers about one half inch. What you will see is a finger that looks like a floating frankfurter.

DO-IT YOURSELF OPTRICKS

Mach's Depth Reversing Figure. Fold a small piece of paper in half on the long side, as shown in the illustration above. Open it just enough to allow it to stand on the table. Close one eye and stare straight down on it. After your one eye adapts to the image, you won't be able to decide whether you are seeing the inside or outside of the folded paper.

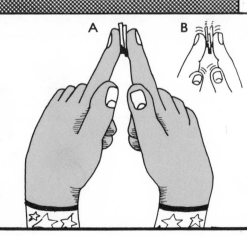

A   B

Ghost Money. Take two pennies and grip them between the tips of your index fingers, holding them vertically (as you see in illustration A). Rub the pennies against each other with short rapid up-and-down movements. A third penny will appear below and between the other two as you see in illustration B.

Mach's Depth Reversing Figure. The explanation for this is simple; by closing one eye, your depth perception is eliminated and you can believe either logical solution. **Floating Frankfurter.** By focusing on a distant point, you prevent the separate images of your fingers from fusing together properly. Your left eye sees part of your right finger and vice versa, forming one small finger, which if you close one eye, will disappear. **Find the Missing Piece of Pie.** Since you almost never see a pie upside down, your mind can't resist the temptation to interpret the ellipses as the side of the pan viewed from above. **Ghost Money.** Your retinas temporarily retain the images of the two coins as they move, creating a third coin. The reason for the ghost penny always appearing below the real coins, has never been satisfactorily explained.

Using only your eye, can you figure out how to mount these cowboys (B) on their horses (A)?

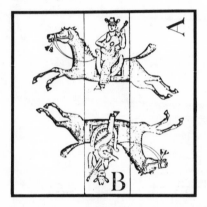

The illusion on page 35 tricks your brain, not your eye. Logic tells you how the cowboys should be mounted on their horses but the solution only proves how deceiving logic can be. Cut out the pieces of this puzzle and try it on your friends.

36

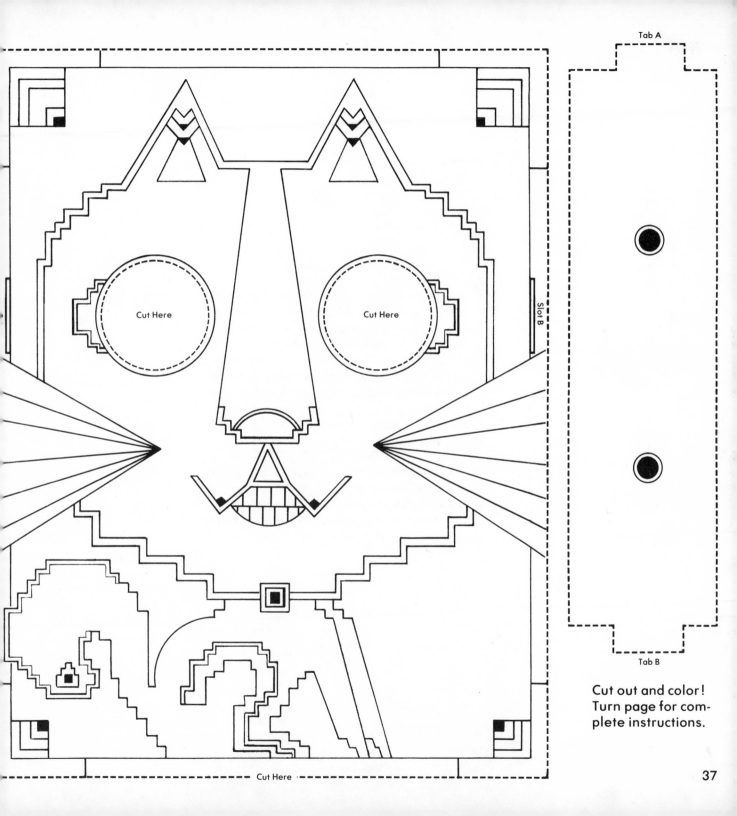

Cut Here

Cut Here

Slot B

Cut Here

Tab A

Tab B

Cut out and color!
Turn page for complete instructions.

Instructions:

1. Cut out the portrait of the cat and cut out the circular eyes on the dotted lines as indicated. 2. Cut out the insert with the cat's pupils on it. 3. Make a slit where it's marked "Slot A" and "Slot B." 4. Put the insert (facing front) to the back of the portrait. 5. Attach Tab A to Slot A and Tab B to Slot B with glue or tape. 6. Pin the picture up on a wall at eye level. 7. Stand about 10 feet away and walk to the left and the right watching the eyes. They seem to follow you around the room! The optical illusion is caused by the placement of the eyeball and eye socket on two different planes combined with the angle at which you view the picture. The eyes seem to move, but actually the viewer does.

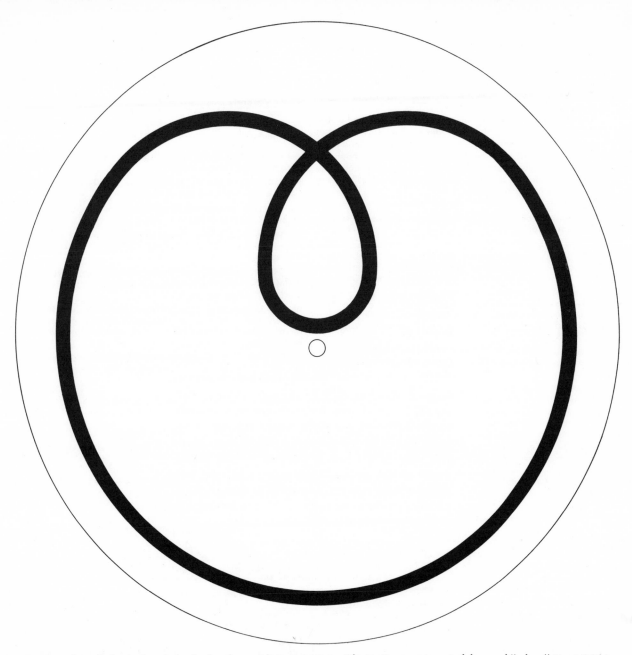

Cut out this disk and poke a hole through its center. Place it on a turntable and "play" it at 33⅓ rpm. The figure will appear to warp as it starts to spin. When the turntable reaches full speed, turn it off. The figure will appear to return to its original shape. This is an adaptation illusion (an illusion which is caused by the over stimulation and resulting fatigue of the retina). The sensation is paradoxical since it is seen as warping, yet the figure always remains the same shape.

The Flip Book: Cinematic motion is an illusion produced by a series of still images flashing rapidly across the screen. The speed (24 frames per second) is so great that your eyes cannot distinguish each separate frame. You will find a simple demonstration of this principle in the "flickers" that appear in the upper left hand corner of every left hand page in this book. Just hold the left hand corner of the book between your thumb and index finger and flip through the pages as rapidly as possible. You will be looking at the very first form of "motion pictures."

Here is some information about the artists whose work is reproduced in this book:

Salvador Dali was born in Spain in 1904. He is a well known and prolific surrealist. As a painter, Dali has made a reputation by creating sensations and employing a mysterious system of symbolism. Dali now lives in New York City with his wife Gala.

Maurits Cornelis Escher was born in Holland in 1898. He spent his life exploring visual illusions and mastering the art of black and white line rendering. Escher employed mathematics, symbolism and a good sense of humor in much of his work. He died in Holland in 1972.

William Hogarth was an Eighteenth Century English engraver. He was most renowned for his satiric portraitures. Hogarth died in 1764.

Rene Magritte was born in Belgium in 1898. He was a master of fantastic art with the unique ability to interpret contemporary society through the use of everyday objects. He achieved his effects through the use of optical illusions. Magritte died in Brussels at the age of 69.

Victor Vasarely was born in Hungary in 1908. As the leading pioneer and outstanding practitioner of "Op" art, he achieves a union of visual imagination with mathematical and scientific principles. Vasarely currently lives in Annet-Sur-Marne, France.

We are grateful to the following for permission to reproduce their optical art in our book:

Pg. 7, 8: Victor Vasarely, **Metagalaxie**. 1960-61. Oil on canvas, 148.6 x 186.7cm. Courtesy of the artist.

Pg. 11, 12: Rene Magritte, **Blank Signature**. Oil on canvas, 31.9 x 25.6cm. Courtesy of ADAGP, Paris.

Pg. 15, 16: M.C. Escher, **Concave and Convex**. Lithograph, 28 x 33cm. Courtesy of the Vorpal Gallery, San Francisco and Chicago.

Pg. 21, 22: **The Computer Gargoyle.** Courtesy of L.D. Harmon and K.C. Knowlton, Bell Telephone Laboratories, Incorporated, Murray Hill, New Jersey.

Pg. 25, 26: Salvador Dali, **Old Age, Adolescence, Infancy (The Three Ages)**. 1940. Oil on canvas, 49.8 x 65.1cm. Courtesy of Mr. and Mrs. A. Reynolds·Morse, Salvador Dali Museum, Cleveland, Ohio.

Pg. 27, 28: M.C. Escher, **Circle Limit IV (Heaven and Hell)**. Woodcut, 41.3cm in diameter. Courtesy of the Vorpal Gallery, San Francisco and Chicago.

A special note of thanks to the **Exploratorium**, San Francisco, for their encouragement and patient cooperation.